Warrior Whale

Books by Joseph J. Cook and William L. Wisner

Warrior Whale
The Phantom World of the Octopus and Squid
Killer Whale!
Your First Book of Salt Water Fishing

A swimming herd of sperm whales. Note whale at upper right slapping surface with flukes

WARRIOR WHALE

By Joseph J. Cook and William L. Wisner

Illustrated with photographs, old prints, and diagrams

DODD, MEAD & COMPANY · NEW YORK

ACKNOWLEDGMENTS

The authors particularly wish to thank the following people who helped make this book possible: The International Association of Whaling Companies, Sandefjord, Norway; The Mariners Museum, Newport News, Virginia; New Zealand Consulate General, New York City; Dr. Ross F. Nigrelli, Director, Osborn Laboratories of Marine Science, New York Aquarium, New York Zoological Society, Adjunct Professor of Biology, New York University; American Museum of Natural History, New York City; Mystic Seaport, Mystic, Connecticut; and the Norwegian Embassy, New York City.

PICTURE CREDITS

Courtesy of: Alexander Turnbull Library, New Zealand, 26 *top*, 41, 44, 49, 51, 60, 73 *left*, 80, 84; The American Museum of Natural History, N.Y., N.Y., 11, 13, 14, 24, 31, 73 *right*, 88, 94; Black Star, N.Y., N.Y., 81, 89; Dr. O. Braekken, Norway, 23 *right*; Jan Cook, 16 *top*, 23 *left*; Fisheries Research Board of Canada, Gordon C. Pike, 16 *bottom* (for permission to use this material contact Fisheries Research Board of Canada, Biological Station, Nanaimo, B.C., refer to Circular 32); Frank W. Lane, Middlesex, England, 19, 20, 78, 93; Givaudan-Delawanna, Inc., N.Y., N.Y., 32; The International Association of Whaling Companies, Masaharu Nishiwaki, The Whales Research Institute, Tokyo, Japan, *frontispiece*, 8, 22, 27, 36, 83; Marine Historical Association, Mystic, Connecticut, 42 *right*, 69, 76 *right*; The Mariners Museum, Newport News, Va., 10, 37, 42 *left*, 47, 53, 55, 57, 59, 62, 63, 65, 66, 67, 71, 74, 76 *left*, 86, 87; New Zealand Consulate General, N.Y., N.Y., 35; Norwegian Embassy, 91; U.S. Department of the Interior, Fish and Wildlife Service, Matt Seralla, 27 *bottom*; The Whaling Museum, New Bedford, Mass., 28.

Library of Congress Catalog Card Number: 66-13346
Printed in the United States of America

This book is dedicated with great affection to our parents,
Ida and the late Joseph Cook, and Lydia and William L. Wisner, Sr.

Introduction

Whales are the largest—and among the most intelligent—wild animals ever to live on our globe. Few creatures in the vast underwater empire covering most of our planet have so aroused man's respect and admiration. And of all those huge marine mammals, the sperm whale or cachalot has figured most prominently in nations' maritime history. The story of this great beast is a colorful, exciting and often violent chapter in man's unceasing efforts to conquer the sea and its inhabitants.

Dr. Ross F. Nigrelli
Director, Osborn Laboratories of Marine Science,
    New York Aquarium, New York Zoological Society
Adjunct Professor of Biology, New York University

Contents

I. The Remote Past

According to the Bible's Old Testament, Jonah was cast into the sea by sailors who believed he was bringing bad fortune to their vessel. The Bible says: "Now the Lord prepared a great fish to swallow up Jonah. And Jonah was in the belly of the fish three days and three nights." Probably the only fish or whale capable of gulping Jonah was the mighty sperm whale or cachalot, the largest of the toothed whales.

In comparatively recent times—the year was 1891—a crewman named James Bartley was reported to have been swallowed alive by a sperm whale. Bartley disappeared inside the whale when the enraged cachalot attacked his whaleboat. The next day, according to one version of the story, the same whale was killed by Bartley's shipmates, and when the great beast was cut open the missing sailor was found inside the animal's stomach, unconscious but still alive. The story goes on to state that Bartley's shipmates were able to revive him and, except for being emotionally unbalanced for a while, he was all right. Until the time that no more was heard of him, Bartley told and retold how it felt to go down a sperm whale's gullet and end up in the monster's stomach.

There has always been an element of doubt about the Bartley tale, and since existing accounts were not obtained from the man himself, that doubt will remain. It has been questionable in the minds of many whether there would be enough oxygen in a whale's stomach to keep a man from suffocating; and, even if there were enough oxygen to

A solitary bull over 55 feet long comes to the surface of the sea
and is photographed from a plane

An old print shows Jonah cast
up by the whale

breathe, whether or not the victim could survive the animal's digestive juices. However, if that story is true, James Bartley is the only man on record to duplicate Jonah's amazing experience.

All whales belong to a group of marine mammals which scientists call cetaceans; a name which comes from the Latin word *cetus*, meaning whale. Although whales live in the sea, have fins and look like giant fish, these bulky residents of the deep are mammals, as are dogs, horses, and men. They are classified as mammals because they are warm-blooded, breathe air with lungs, give birth to living young, and nurse their offspring with milk.

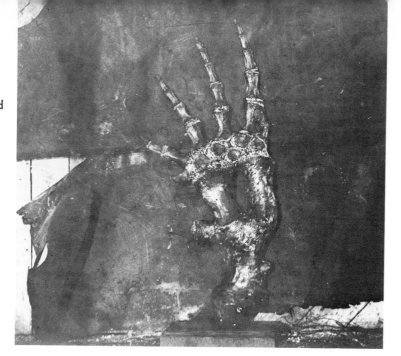

Flipper of sperm whale stripped of blubber, Vancouver Island

Cetaceans have been in the world for a long, long time. Scientists tell us they inhabited our globe many millions of years before the first human being trod the earth.

Studies of fossil remains and the rocks containing them tell a fascinating story. Experts believe that in a dim past, more than a hundred million years ago, the ancestors of all cetaceans were land animals. It is believed that the day came when some of the whale's early ancestors ventured into the water, perhaps in search of food, or to elude enemies. At first they stayed in the water only a short time. What they found there they liked, so next time they remained in the water a little longer. Finally they adjusted to the ocean so well that they stayed in it continually, never to go ashore as other marine mammals, such as seals and walruses, do.

Countless centuries passed during which whale's bodies became more streamlined so they could slide through the water more easily. Their limbs, also, underwent changes. When they lived on land they needed legs to carry them, but legs are not as good as flippers or fins for balance and steering in the water. Because they were no longer needed to support the body, the hind legs became smaller, finally disappearing almost completely. Most important, the whales slowly developed broad tails with two flukes to propel their huge bodies through the water. The tails of fish are vertical and move from side to side, but the flattened flukes of the whale are horizontal and move up and down.

There were still other changes. When the cetaceans' ancestors lived on land their bodies probably had hair or fur for warmth and protection. In water such coverings slowed down the animals, so gradually the skins became smooth. With their protective hair gone, the early whales required still another adaptation to maintain body heat. That came in the form of blubber, a layer of fat between the animals' outer skin and the flesh. Even the nostrils or blowholes changed from a location far forward in the snout to the top of their heads, making it easier for them to breathe at the water's surface. Through all these years of change, known as evolution, whales still kept their lungs.

Fish take oxygen from the water through their gills, but whales hold their breath underwater as a man does and must come to the surface of the sea to breathe. If they did not do this they would drown.

When underwater, whales keep their nostrils or blowholes tightly closed. During the time the animal is submerged the warm air in its lungs becomes saturated with

Skeleton of large
sperm whale

water vapor. As the whale's head leaves the water it opens its blowholes to force out
the carbon dioxide from the lungs. When this strikes the cool outer air it condenses
and forms a column of vapor, which may shoot up twenty feet in the air. This is known
as blowing or spouting.

Whales are divided into two major groups: the baleen whales and the toothed
whales. Baleen whales have large mouths, small throats, no teeth, and double blowholes. These great animals feed on tiny organisms called plankton, and small shrimp-
like creatures called krill, which drift in the ocean like a thick soup. Toothed whales
have a single blowhole and from one to fifty or more teeth, depending upon the species. They are mainly flesh eaters.

Ages ago, it is believed, baleen whales had teeth and probably ate fish. As time
went on, however, their feeding habits changed. They began to eat such small things
that their teeth were not needed. Gradually, a growth called baleen formed in their
mouths to aid them in catching the tiny organisms that became their diet.

Model of a sperm whale

Although baleen is called whalebone, it is not bone. It is a horny substance something like fingernails. It hangs down from the roof of the mouth in two rows, like curtains. The inner edges of the baleen are worn down into bristles which act as a strainer. When water rushes into the mouth, the tongue, which may weigh a ton, presses the water out, leaving krill, plankton, and even small fishes trapped on the bristles. Included in the baleen group are: the bowhead, right whale, finback, humpback, and the blue whale, largest known animal ever to inhabit our planet. The blue whale often measures one hundred feet in length, with a weight of 120 to 150 tons.

Toothed whales, on the other hand, have peglike teeth which are well suited to seizing prey; and, since their food is larger than that of the baleens, they possess wider throats. Included in this group are bottlenose whales, the narwhal, the beluga, the killer, and the sperm whale or cachalot. The sperm whale is the largest of the toothed group and his scientific name is *Physeter catadon*.

The great Leviathan that maketh the sea to seethe
like boiling pan . . . Lord Bacon's Version of the Psalms

2. The Sperm Whale

Most whales are dark in color. Cachalots are black, or a dark slate-gray, with a few areas of white or gray-white on the undersides. Sometimes, although not commonly, there is an all white or albino sperm whale.

Male whales of any species are known as bulls. The females are called cows, and the babies of the family are known as calves. Among sperm whales the mature bulls can attain lengths in excess of fifty feet and weights of fifty tons or more. Exceptional specimens grow seventy-five to eighty feet long and weigh up to seventy tons. In the sperm whale family, as so often occurs among animals, the males are larger than the females. Cow sperm whales generally are shorter than forty feet and weigh less than fifty tons.

A particularly interesting physical detail of the sperm whale is revealed if we view one from the side. This outstanding feature is the great size of the head. Rectangular and box-shaped, the cachalot's massive head takes up about one-third of the animal's total length. Thus, if a specimen is fifty feet long, the head measures more than sixteen feet.

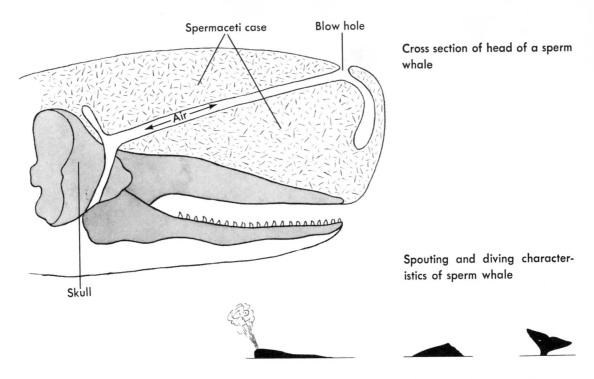

Spermaceti case

Blow hole

Cross section of head of a sperm whale

Air

Skull

Spouting and diving characteristics of sperm whale

It is in the head that we also find the origin of this whale's name, because here is located an extraordinary "storage tank" which contains a glistening, oily, waxlike substance called spermaceti. From this fatty substance was derived the word "sperm" and thus the name. The large storage tank consists of a certain kind of tissue which contains fat cells carrying the spermaceti.

Spermaceti is lighter than water, and for a long time it was believed that the whale's reservoir of the material served as a kind of buoyancy apparatus when diving or returning to the sea's surface. Now it is thought that the spermaceti may have something to do with the cachalot's phenomenal ability to dive deep and then ascend to the surface relatively quickly, without suffering the "bends," an affliction which attacks human divers when they surface from a dive too rapidly.

In humans the ailment known as the bends is caused by a too rapid decrease in pressure. When a man dives deep he must breathe air under pressure. That pressure causes nitrogen to be dissolved in his blood stream. If he returns to the surface too fast, the pressure is decreased too rapidly, with the result that the nitrogen, no longer kept in solution, forms bubbles in his blood, just as the carbonating gas in soda pop bubbles out when the cap is removed. Bubbles in the blood stream can clog veins and arteries, damage vital organs, and cause the victim to writhe in terrible pain. If severe enough, the bends can kill. That is why human divers returning from the depths must ascend slowly, to allow their blood to adjust to the pressure which decreases as they rise. Divers also often have a decompression chamber aboard their ships which accomplishes the same thing. Gradually it decreases the pressure under which men breathe so that any dissolved nitrogen can be removed normally through the lungs instead of bubbling out in the blood stream.

A sperm whale can dive to great depths and return to the sea's surface soon afterward to breathe without suffering these ill effects. Since spermaceti can absorb about six times more nitrogen than the whale's blood, it is thought that this greatly reduces the chances of any nitrogen forming bubbles in the animal's blood.

Sperm whales also are aided in their deep dives by other factors. In the first place, they start off by having much less nitrogen in their lungs than do land animals. When they dive, most of the oxygen and other gases are forced out of their lungs through the blowholes by the increasing water pressure surrounding their bodies. This also reduces the amount of nitrogen which is absorbed by the blood stream.

Another aid to their deep diving and their ability to remain submerged for an appreciable time is the cachalots' superior ability to oxygenate their blood—that is, supply it with oxygen when they come up to breathe. They are much better at this than humans are. Sperm whales can renew 90 per cent of their oxygen supply when breathing, whereas humans renew only about 20 per cent with each breath.

Finally, the rate of the heartbeat drops abruptly when they go into their dives, and this also is believed to be a factor in preventing the bends in sperm whales.

Cachalots are possibly the greatest diving creatures in existence, descending to depths far beyond the reach of any other known surface-living creature and certainly any other air breather we know. Even the deepest-swimming fishes cannot duplicate this feat, for the fishes living at great depths are adjusted to water pressure at those levels. If they rise too far, the decreasing pressure kills them.

Sperm whales can descend as deep as a half-mile or more. In 1932, the cable repair ship *All America*, investigating the failure of an undersea cable between Panama and Guayaquil, Ecuador, found the cable wrapped around the skeleton of a cachalot which had been trapped at a depth of 3,500 feet. The vessel's first mate said that almost two hundred feet of cable had twisted around the ill-fated animal's remains. Part of the cable, he said, had caught in the victim's jaw, and the rest had twisted around his tail, indicating a dive of more than half a mile.

It is easy to see how a chain or cable could become caught on the long narrow jaw of a sperm whale

More than a dozen similar cases have been reported. Eight occurred off the American Pacific Coast; one each was recorded for the waters off Nova Scotia, for the Persian Gulf, for an area off Cape Frio, Brazil; and two elsewhere off the coasts of South America. In six of the instances, the cable was 3,150 feet deep. In the others, sperm whales had run afoul of the cables at depths ranging from 350 to 1,225 feet.

As already stated, all whales, save a single species, have the blowholes located high atop the head, in the center and well back from the snout, where they are in the best position to breathe when the head comes out of the water. The one exception is the

The single, s-shaped blowhole of the cachalot is located on the left side of head near the snout. All other whales have blowholes high atop their heads

cachalot. Its single blowhole, more or less S-shaped, is invariably on the port or left side of the head and located near the snout. Its unusual position is probably due in part to the rectangular shape of the head.

When a sperm whale comes up slowly to breathe, it approaches the surface almost parallel to it, in a manner reminiscent of a surfacing submarine. When the head emerges from the sea, the animal opens its blowhole and forces out the stale air.

Whales not only surface to breathe, they also come up to sleep. There they drowse, their blowholes out of water. The sperm whale appears to be the deepest sleeper of all the cetaceans. Several observers have stated that these gigantic creatures can stay near the surface for hours on end, apparently in deep slumber. That cachalots are indeed sound sleepers is borne out by many stories of ships colliding with them.

One dark night during World War II, a United States destroyer suddenly shuddered under a heavy jolt, then rapidly lost speed. Thinking they had been torpedoed, her crew took to the lifeboats; and then it was discovered that there was no torpedo damage. Next morning the body of a large, dead cachalot was found across the destroyer's bow.

A similarly violent contact with a sleeping sperm whale was experienced by the steamship *Amerskerk*, commanded by Captain A. P. Disselkoen, on March 22, 1955. The vessel was making a lively seventeen knots at sea when she collided with something. Damage-control investigation revealed that she had struck a 32-foot cachalot. The ship had to go astern, or back up, to free herself from the animal, which had been killed on impact.

It seems likely that napping sperm whales also collided with the 24,000 ton American luxury liner *Constitution* off Genoa, Italy; the Russian whaler *Aleut* near the Panama Canal; and the vessel *William Ruys* at sea between South Africa and Ceylon. The cachalots' habit of snoozing near the ocean's surface undoubtedly has caused a number of collision accidents over the years.

Several other of the sperm whale's distinguishing features seem to be centered about the head. Along with its extraordinary size, the tank of spermaceti it contains, and the location of the blowhole, a detail which sets the head of the cachalot apart from other cetaceans is its long, narrow jaw. The lower jaw is armed with eighteen

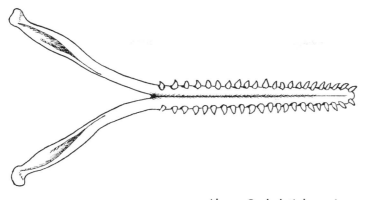

Above: Cachalot's lower jaw
Right: Interesting photograph shows teeth in lower jaw of sperm whale, which fit into indentations in upper jaw

to thirty pairs of teeth which are shaped like pegs and measure about eight inches long by four inches wide each. The teeth lie imbedded in a groove, firmly held in position in such a way that, when the mouth is closed, their conical, ivory-colored tip sections fit exactly into a row of corresponding indentations in the palate of the whale's upper jaw. Oddly enough, the sperm whale's fine set of teeth does not play as important a part in its feeding habits as their number and development might indicate. The teeth often are covered with barnacles, showing that there is a significant amount of disuse; and they frequently show signs of decay and disease. The fact is, cachalots probably use their teeth chiefly for seizing and holding prey, rather than chewing, because they swallow their food whole.

Resting herd of sperm whales. Several whales are standing on their tails

Note blowhole on end of snout and tiny eye socket of this dead cachalot

The cachalot's brain weighs twenty pounds, which is not spectacular in relation to its size, or when comparing the organ with the brain of man, which averages three pounds, or that of an elephant, which has a maximum weight of eleven pounds. However, cetaceans in general are considered intelligent animals and the sperm whale's brain is the largest, by weight, of all mammals.

The sperm whale's small eyes also seem out of proportion to its great size. The smallness of its optic organs, coupled with the fact that it dives into the darkness of great depths for giant squids, lead scientists to assume that the cachalot does not rely solely on sight to locate prey. It is believed that it is aided to a large extent in finding food and in navigating the inky blackness of the deeps by a type of built-in radar. Keenness of hearing, second only to that of bats, plays an important role.

A common experience will help illustrate how a sperm whale's "radar" operates. If

24

you are in mountainous country and call out loudly, the sound waves of your voice will travel until they strike a hill, literally bounce off it, and return to you as an echo. The cachalot's echo-sounding mechanism functions in similar fashion.

As the whale cruises it emits a series of squeaks. The sounds radiate outward in many directions, traveling faster and farther than they would in the air. When they strike a solid object, such as a giant squid or the ocean bottom, they bounce off it like an echo and return to the whale, to be caught by its keen sense of hearing. By gauging the time interval between transmitting the squeaks and receiving their echo, a kind of "computer" in the cachalot's brain enables it to locate the object accurately. Thus the whale can pinpoint prey and, when navigating, detect obstructions in its way.

The tremendous heart of a cachalot is almost six feet wide, and its weight is such that the strength of several men is required to lift it. The need for such a large heart is understandable when you consider that the vital organ must pump hundreds of gallons of blood through hundreds of miles of arteries and veins. Even more impressive is the length of a sperm whale's intestinal tract. In a live, fifty-five foot specimen, it measures about five hundred feet; when relaxed after death it can extend to as long as twelve hundred feet.

Despite their bulk, sperm whales are fast swimmers, propelled by their tremendously strong tails. These remarkable tails, being deeply notched in the middle, form two equally sized parts known as flukes. These flukes, powered by the tail's strong muscles, form a highly efficient pair of sculls or oars which operate in a double, semi-rotary action, making figure of eight motions, the effect of which is very much like that of a two-bladed propeller on a boat. Cachalots have been observed cruising at speeds ranging from eight to twenty knots. Since a knot, the nautical unit of velocity, is approximately one and one-eighth miles per hour, this means that these whales can achieve speeds of nine to twenty-two miles an hour, which is faster than some boats and ships can go. Sperm whales are known to attain twenty knots in short spurts, then settle down to an average speed of ten knots.

In addition to being a superb swimmer, the cachalot is capable of thrusting its body clear of the sea. In such acrobatics it is the powerful tail which serves as the power plant. Because of its great bulk, the sea giant finds it difficult to leap completely clear of the waves and many times in such displays about half of the body remains submerged. When the jumps are more spectacular, the tail can be seen beating the water in a vertical position. If you have ever tried to lift part of your body clear of the water while swimming, you can appreciate how much strength must be required to lift thirty tons or more.

Cachalot calves, it appears, are born at any time of the year. A mother carries her baby for sixteen months before the infant has developed sufficiently to be released into the world. Then, for six months thereafter, she protects it against harm, aided by the bulls in the community. A cow usually produces a baby no oftener than once every three years.

A newborn sperm whale measures up to fourteen feet in length. Like other infants in the animal kingdom, the newcomer to the family is dependent upon his mother for food during the very first phase of life in the outside world, and, like other mammalian mothers, the cachalot nurses her baby with milk. Suckling is accomplished at the

26

Sperm whales in a circle. They have been observed to take this formation, like a wagon train, when attacked, slapping the sea surface into foam with their tails

Reproduction of a watercolor, "Cow Whale and Calf," c. 1840. The mother whale is attempting to save her calf which has been harpooned and is sinking

surface of the sea, because the calves must breathe. The milk is rich and nourishing, and growth responds accordingly. The calves are over twenty feet in length when weaned and appear to be fully adult at three years of age.

Predominantly tropical animals, with a preference for the vast expanse of ocean between 40° north and 40° south latitudes, cachalots will migrate just as regularly as other kinds of whales in search of food. Many of these travels are on a grand scale, covering thousands of miles in a wide, semicircular sweep. The far-flung searches for food usually are made in a clockwise direction. This, at first, seems unusual, since ocean currents follow a counterclockwise course in southern oceans. The whales are actually traveling against the currents. But it is not so unusual when you consider the probability that, by swimming into the currents rather than with them, the animals are in a better position to capture food being swept along by those currents practically into their mouths.

Authorities have an interesting theory about the way sperm whales lure their prey. As they cruise along with their mouths open, squids and cuttlefish seem to be attracted by the colorful contrast between the cachalot's purple tongue and the whiteness of the jaw's gums. Squids and cuttlefish apparently cannot resist that contrast in colors.

As squids and cuttlefish often abound where cold currents meet tropical water, the southwestern coast of Africa and South America's western seaboard teem with these creatures. Here may be found huge gams (schools or herds) of sperm whales. Although small gams migrate to the Arctic and Antarctic waters in the summer, these are usually composed of mature bulls which have failed to become leaders of small communities of cows and calves.

As you can imagine, much food is required to nourish a sperm whale's huge body, and the great beast has an appetite in proportion to its size. Although squids and their relative the cuttlefish comprise the main portion of a cachalot's diet, assorted items have been found in cachalot stomachs, including small fishes of various kinds, sharks as long as ten feet, and even seals.

There are many species of squids, and they range in size from those only a few inches long on up to the giant *Architeuthis*, which is believed to attain lengths of fifty feet or more. *Architeuthis* inhabits depths of fifteen hundred feet and deeper, and is indeed a nightmarish creature. Like other squids, he is equipped with eight arms and two long, slender tentacles. All these appendages have powerful sucking disks for seizing and holding prey. Hidden in among these writhing arms is a sharp beak, shaped like that of a parrot. This beak can cut through heavy wire and tough wood, and it tears victims to shreds. The giant squid is a fearsome and formidable creature.

However, he holds no terror for the sperm whale, and a cachalot will dive to great depths to search for *Architeuthis*. Round scars, sucker marks from a giant squid's arms, often are found on the skins of captured sperm whales, providing evidence of combat. Some of these scars are practically the size of saucers, indicating the size of the cachalots' opponents.

Very few men have witnessed the fight to the death of a cachalot and a giant squid. Even fewer are the men who, having been a witness to such an encounter, thought to write down an account of the struggle. However, one mariner did. He was Frank T. Bullen, an English seaman and author. He described his firsthand view of the battle in his famous book *The Cruise of the Cachalot*.

One of the most amazing feats performed by the cachalot is the swallowing of a giant squid whole. At a whaling station in the Azores, Robert Clarke of England's National Institute of Oceanography, a foremost authority on sperm whales, once opened a cachalot to find a giant squid about thirty-five feet long, weighing more than

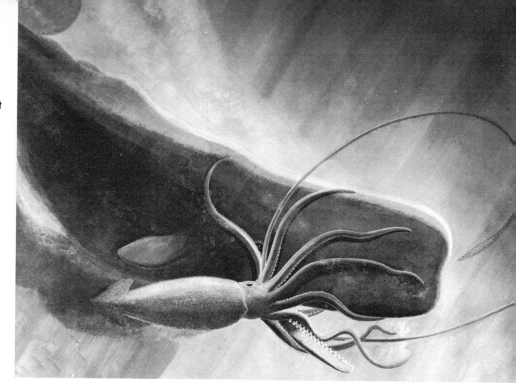

Battle between a sperm whale and a giant squid, from a painting

five hundred pounds. On record are other instances of thirty to thirty-five foot specimens being discovered inside sperm whales. In at least one case, the ill-fated victim was still alive.

It is the sperm whale's fondness for giant squids which brings about the creation of one of the sea's most valuable products. Although the cachalot can and does swallow those lengthy creatures whole, he cannot digest their hard, parrot-like beaks. Sometimes the undigested beak fails to pass through the animal's intestinal tract and causes the formation of a sticky, darkish-colored substance around it. This is the material

This piece of ambergris weighed 15½ pounds and was valued at $20,000 in 1956

known as ambergris. Strangely enough, though ambergris may be quite foul-smelling, it is highly desirable in the manufacture of good perfumes, the reason being that it helps to hold the scent better.

Sperm whales often are able to rid themselves of this substance by spewing it out, after which it is found in chunks of varying size floating at sea or cast upon beaches. Sometimes whaling men find ambergris inside a cachalot when cutting up the carcass. However, relatively little ambergris is found anywhere; and its scarcity, coupled with the demand for it in the making of perfumes, causes it to be very valuable.

There Leviathan,
Hugest of living creatures, in the deep
Stretched like a promontory, sleeps or swims,
And seems a moving land; and at his gills
Draws in, and at his breath spouts out a sea . . . Paradise Lost

3. Cachalot at Sea

Thus, three centuries ago, did the great English poet John Milton describe a whale. It is a dramatic description, but the poet is inaccurate when he mentions "gills." Obviously he did not know that whales are lung breathers and do not have gills. But he is quite right in other details: "Stretched like a promontory . . . And seems a moving land. . . ." A full-grown bull cachalot is indeed a small isle in the sea, and the hump-like ridge on his back could be likened to a mountain or a promontory on that isle.

Sperm whales have few enemies besides the giant squid. Man is the worst foe, since encounters with him usually lead to death. Other enemies include packs of killer whales, and, for the males, each other, when cows are involved.

Male sperm whales do not take a single mate but select a number of females, as many as twenty or thirty. Such a harem is acquired by force, with the bulls ramming heads and exchanging vicious bites to gain their mates.

Acquiring a personal collection of cows is one thing; keeping them is still another. Other males may try to lure them away; younger bulls may attack the master of the harem to challenge his leadership. A male cachalot with a group of females is a jealous mate and will defend his cows with all his cunning, strength, and experience. Once a bull has been defeated in battle by another male, the females leave him for the victor. Witnesses who have observed bull cachalots in combat for a harem describe it as a battle of giants bent on destruction.

A bull that loses such a skirmish is known as an "old bachelor." But that defeat does not mean that he cannot take care of himself. He still has the power of self-preservation, of hunting or of fighting for prey, and can look forward to many years of life in the sea. Lone bulls are not animals to be trifled with. Although normally shy, male cachalots become aggressive after they have been driven away from their wives and community. Usually this change in temperament is accompanied by an urge to travel; and bachelor bulls of all ages migrate alone or in their own groups to the waters of the Arctic and Antarctic.

The cachalot's most persistent "foes," and certainly the most annoying, are the small creatures grouped under the name parasite. As we know, except for bachelor bulls, sperm whales prefer the warm expanses of the ocean. In these waters also live parasites known as whale lice, some of which grow to the size of walnuts. Few things can make life more miserable for the cachalot than whale lice when they bore through the skin and dig deep into the blubber underneath. Barnacles and other parasites cling to the lips and corners of the whale's mouth, causing pain to these tender spots. No matter how much their host shakes his big head, the pricking and

A closeup of those annoying parasites, barnacles, on the tail of a humpback whale

itching cause discomfort. A sperm whale in the vicinity of a ship or a large wreck sometimes will rub himself against it in an effort to get rid of troublesome parasitic pests.

Despite displays of bad temper and aggressiveness, plus a reputation among whalers of being truly dangerous when injured or aroused, cachalots are known to be playful animals. On August 10, 1955, the steamship *Akkrumdijk* witnessed such an incident. The vessel approached a gam of fourteen sperm whales near the surface. Most of the animals swam away as the *Akkrumdijk* neared them, but one remained behind. He had found a large, drifting plank, and he stayed to play with it, swimming around it and diving close beneath it, in several repeat performances.

Among cachalots as well as whales of other species there occurs a mysterious phenomenon which thus far has defied a proven explanation. It is the mass strandings of the great beasts on beaches. In such strandings, a dozen, two dozen, or more of the animals may be found unable to escape the shallows of a beach.

No one knows for certain why this occurs. Scientists believe that panic may be the cause in certain instances. It is thought that when the whales suddenly find themselves in shallow water they become panicky and in that excited state are unable to find their way out to deeper water. Other factors contributing to mass strandings may be abrupt temperature changes and sudden, violent thunderstorms, either of

Engraving of whale stranded on Holland Coast, by Jan Saenredam, 1602.

which might cause a kind of panic among whales. Many incidents of strandings of cachalots and other species have been recorded over the years. On March 14, 1784, thirty-two sperm whales were stranded on a South Brittany coast in France. More recently, on February 24, 1954, thirty-four cachalots were found trapped on the beach at La Paz, California. Two weeks earlier, at the same location, twenty-four of the animals ran aground.

Death comes to stranded whales through a form of suffocation. They are literally crushed to death. In the water much of the whale's bulk is buoyed up, but stranded on a beach, that support is removed and the animal's weight presses down on its lungs to interfere with breathing. Then the victim suffocates.

Perhaps research someday will discover why these huge animals allow themselves to be panicked into suicide on a beach. Until then this remains a mystery to heighten our interest in cetaceans.

With his great size, formidable teeth, aggressiveness, and endurance, the sperm whale has aptly earned the whalers' name of "warrior whale."

Herd of sperm whales playing with large timber. Third whale from
left bites timber while others chase him. Note wide open blowholes
on some whales, and spouts

An early representation of a sperm whale on the beach

The decaying body of a sperm whale on the beach in Washington State

4. Rogue Sperm Whales

Normally a sperm whale fights only when angered by attack or injury by a foe, and even then it is often a case of frantic desperation. However, when a bull cachalot leads a solitary existence, usually occasioned by his being driven away from a gam, his fighting abilities are sharpened. What is more, enforced exile as a "loner" does nothing to improve his temper, as many a whaling man learned at his peril in the days of hand-thrown harpoons. There is still other danger from the brutes. As among elephants, there is the occasional so-called rogue, a solitary bull and an outcast from whale society, characterized by a vicious temper and unpredictable aggressiveness. Rogue cachalots are especially dangerous as compared to other rogue animals.

How dangerous they can be is illustrated by the savage attack of a rogue on the whaler *Essex* on November 20, 1820. Herman Melville used the incident as the basis for his account of the ramming of the vessel *Pequod* in his immortal chronicle of whaling, *Moby Dick*.

The *Essex*, 238 tons, sailed from Nantucket on August 12, 1819, with provisions for two and a half years at sea. After stopping in the Azores she proceeded into the South Atlantic and rounded Cape Horn in December of that year. By October of

1820 she had reached the Galapagos Islands. The following month, on a lonely expanse of the Pacific Ocean some two thousand miles west of the Galapagos, the vessel met a shuddering end at the head of an enraged rogue cachalot.

Owen Chase, first mate of the ill-starred ship, wrote an exciting account of the attack and the whaler's final moments before her journey to Davey Jones's locker. At the time of the attack Chase was aboard the *Essex*, in command, while her master, Captain George Pollard, was in a whaleboat pursuing a sperm. Suddenly, Chase said, he noticed ". . . a very large spermaceti whale, as well as I could judge about eighty-five feet in length; he broke water about twenty rods off our weather bow, and was lying quietly, with his head in a direction for the ship. He spouted two or three times, and then disappeared. In less than two or three seconds he came up again, about the length of the ship off, and made directly for us, at the rate of about three knots. The ship then was going with about the same velocity. His appearance and attitude gave us at first no alarm; but while I stood watching his movements, and observing him but a ship's length off, coming down for us with great celerity, I involuntarily ordered the boy at the helm to put it up hard, intending to sheer off and avoid him. The words were scarcely out of my mouth, before he came down upon us with full speed, and struck the ship with his head, just forward of the fore chains; he gave such an appalling and tremendous jar, as nearly threw us all on our faces. The ship brought up as suddenly and violently as if she had struck a rock, and trembled for a few seconds like a leaf. We looked at each other with perfect amazement, deprived almost of the power of speech. Many minutes elapsed before we were able to realize the terrible incident; during which time he passed under the ship, grazing her keel as he

Normally a sperm whale fights only when angered by attack or injury. It is sometimes difficult in these early pictures to determine just what type of whale an artist wishes to convey. The cachalots are usually identifiable by the single spout or the teeth

went along, came up alongside her to leeward, and lay on top of the water (apparently stunned with the violence of the blow) for the space of a minute; he then suddenly started off, in a direction to leeward. After a few minutes' reflection, and recovering, in some measure, from the sudden consternation that had seized us, I of course concluded that he had stove a hole in the ship, and that it would be necessary to set the pumps going. Accordingly they were rigged, but had not been in operation more than one minute before I perceived the head of the ship to be gradually settling down in the water; I then ordered the signal to be set for the other boats, which, scarcely had I dispatched, before I again discovered the whale, apparently in convulsions, on top of the water, about one hundred rods to leeward. He was enveloped

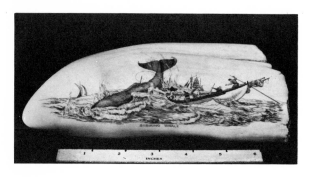

Scrimshaw carving showing harpooning of a cachalot. The whale that sank the *Essex* destroyed not the small whaleboat but the ship herself

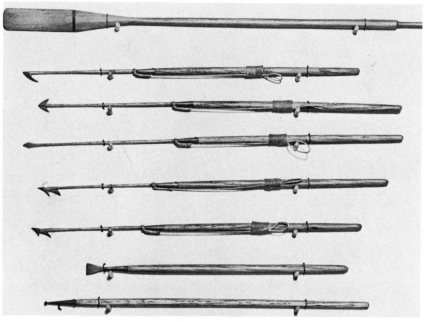

Early harpoons and handles

in the foam of the sea, that his continual and violent thrashing about in the water had created around him, and I could distinctly see him smite his jaws together, as if distracted with rage and fury. He remained a short time in this situation, and then started off with great velocity, across the bow of the ship. By this time the ship had settled down a considerable distance in the water, and I gave her up for lost. I, however, ordered the pumps to be kept constantly going, and endeavored to collect my thoughts for the occasion. I turned to the boats, two of which we then had with the ship, with an intention of clearing them away, and getting all things ready to embark them, if there should be no recourse left; and while my attention was thus engaged for a moment, I was aroused with a cry of a man at the hatchway, 'Here he is—he is making for us again!' I turned around, and saw him about one hundred rods directly ahead of us, coming down apparently with twice his ordinary speed, and to me at that moment, it appeared with tenfold fury and vengeance in his aspect. The surf flew in all directions about him, and his course toward us was marked by a white foam of a rod in width, which he made with the continual violent thrashing of his tail; his head was about half out of water, and in that way he came upon us, and again struck the ship.

"I should judge the speed of the ship to have been at this time three knots, and that of the whale about six. He struck her to windward, directly under the cathead (a projecting timber near the bow), and completely stove in her bows. He passed under the ship again, went off to leeward, and we saw no more of him.

"Every fact seemed to warrant me in concluding that it was anything but chance which directed his operation; he made two severe attacks upon the ship, at a short interval between them, both of which, according to their direction, were calculated to do us the most injury, by being made ahead, and thereby combining the speed of the two objects for the shock. . . . His aspect was most horrible, and such as indicated resentment and fury."

It is evident from Mr. Chase's account that he believed the sperm whale knew exactly what he was doing and did, in fact, want to destroy the *Essex*.

Jaws like a gigantic pair of shears

Twenty men abandoned the stricken vessel in three open boats, led by Captain Pollard and the first mate. Somehow their badly battered ship, her bow smashed, managed to stay afloat for two days, during which time the men were able to salvage some provisions. They then set out across a vast expanse of ocean. Only eight of the twenty survived the terrible journey. These, including the captain and the first mate, returned to their home port of Nantucket on June 11, 1821.

Although not all stories matched that of the survivors of the *Essex*, there were many which attested to the violence of encounters with rogue sperm whales. Among them is the adventure of the New Bedford whaler *Hector*.

The year was 1832. The *Hector* had put out her boats to do battle with a big cachalot, a true prize if they could capture him. Abruptly the infuriated bull turned savagely on the whaleboat commanded by the *Hector*'s mate, his jaws opened like a gigantic pair of shears, and he crushed the craft, hurling screaming men into the water. Seeing their plight, the whaler's skipper, Captain John O. Morse, hastily directed his boat to the scene. His men strained at their oars, the steerer trying to maneuver for a harpoon shot. Before an iron could be thrown, however, the enraged giant charged again. Rolling on his side to better use his jaws, the monster clamped the second boat in his teeth, literally standing it on end above water and shaking it viciously. The crew was plummeted into the sea. Captain Morse, who had been in the stern at that moment, fell some thirty feet.

The heads of the survivors bobbed like corks in the foaming water, each man clinging to whatever wreckage came his way, horrified that the enraged animal made no attempt to move off. The men looked in dismay at the snapping jaws, which at that time were confining their malevolence to a wooden keg.

Now a third whaleboat tried to approach the cachalot unnoticed. The sneak attack failed. Even on the *Hector*, standing by some distance away, could be heard the awful sound of the whale's jaws as he turned to face this new antagonist. His huge, box-like head pushed the sea aside in waves as he charged the boat. Her crew, understandably, was terrified to see this jaw-gnashing animal coming at them. Desperately the oarsmen backed water to turn the boat, then rowed for their lives. The cachalot gave chase, coming so close astern they could smell the foul odor of his breath. That, they thought, was their doom. For some reason, however, the rogue momentarily changed course. The alert boat steerer saw a chance. Bracing himself, he drove his lance deep into the animal's throat, twisting the steel with all his might until the bull spouted blood and died.

An account of the incident in the *Vineyard Gazette*, a contemporary newspaper on Martha's Vineyard, reported: "Captain Morse freely confessed that he never before nor since has come into contact with such an ugly customer as this rogue whale. He seemed to possess the spirit of a demon, and looked as savage as a hungry hyena. Our readers may imagine the effect such an encounter would have upon a crew of 'green hands.' During the frightful chase of the boat by the whale their faces were a livid whiteness and their hair stood erect. On their arrival at the first port, they all took to the mountains."

Another chilling story from the sailing ship era of sperming involves a Long Island whaler skippered by one Captain R. Huntting of Southampton. Captain Huntting ordered boats to give chase to an old bull cachalot that had been sighted. Within minutes of leaving the ship the roles of hunter and intended victims were suddenly reversed. The whale charged both boats violently, mauling each in turn with his jaws, then finishing the job by smashing what was left of the craft with his mighty tail. Struggling in the choppy sea, the shouting men attempted to avoid the crushing blows from the tail's big flukes as they flayed the water. In desperation two of the men seized an opportunity to escape the fearsome tail by scrambling onto the rogue's back. There they clung, for the moment at least, to the creature.

Captain Huntting, in a third whaleboat which had moved into the arena, had little time to contemplate the fantastic scene. Almost immediately the bull attacked again,

The deck of the New Bedford whaling vessel *Kathleen,* looking forward. The *Kathleen* was sunk by a sperm whale in 1901, off the coast of South America

fragments of wood from the other two boats still protruding from his jaws. He struck the small vessel savagely, "like a hurricane, scattering all hands right and left," and catapulted her men into the churned-up sea. Then, satisfied with his destruction, the victorious giant departed the scene. As for the crew in general, this had been their first attempt to kill a whale, and, so far as they were concerned, it also was the last. As soon as their ship fetched port for re-equipping, they quickly deserted.

A number of other attacks by rogue cachalots are in the records. In 1842 alone, the *Yankee* out of New Bedford, the Scottish whaler *Grieff* out of Glasgow, and the English ship *Dudley* all had whaleboats destroyed by irate bulls. In August of 1851, the New Bedford whaler *Ann Alexandra* reportedly was sunk by a cachalot.

Even modern whale catchers can expect trouble from the big brutes. In December of 1955, when the 714-ton Dutch whaler *Johannes W. Vinke* was in the Antarctic, she was rammed by a cachalot. The beast did not sink the vessel, but it put her propeller out of action and she had to be towed to Melbourne, Australia, for repairs.

Perhaps the most notorious of all rogue sperm whales was Mocha Dick, so called, it is said, because his career of mayhem began off the Pacific Island of Mocha. Legend and fact are so closely intertwined that now it is debatable as to whether Mocha Dick really existed or was a figment of whale hunters' imaginations. Tales about the great rogue varied considerable. But in one detail they were consistent, and that was when they came to his terrible ferocity, which was matched only by his cunning. Strangely enough, though, what seemed to horrify his hunters most was Mocha Dick's color. Instead of the usual black or near-black of his breed, he was pale, described variously as deathly white, half-white or gray, and dazzlingly white. Unfortunately, we never learn what finally happened to Mocha Dick, but if we can subscribe to all the tales of his destruction of whaleboats he had a murderous career.

Moby Dick, the terrible-tempered rogue that triumphed over Captain Ahab and the whaler *Pequod*, was an albino. Though a creature of author Herman Melville's imagination, Moby Dick has had modern real-life counterparts. One was a sperm whale harpooned by a killer vessel working with the whaler *Anglo-Norse*, commanded

A whale attacking a boat, from *The Whaleman's Adventure* by Reverend W. Scoresby

by a Captain Pelliet, in the Pacific on August 12, 1951. This animal, fifty-four feet long and estimated at fifty-five tons, had a hide described as being white as snow. Six years later, on April 19, 1957, in waters off Japan, another albino sperm whale was harpooned.

Other cachalots which have achieved a measure of notoriety in whaling history were named Timor Tim (for a Pacific Isle), Don Miguel (Chile), Morguan (Japan), New Zealand Jack, and Newfoundland Tom. They became legendary because of the reported havoc they wrecked among whaleboats, sailors, and even ships.

In his book *The Cruise of the Cachalot*, Frank T. Bullen narrates thrilling stories about some of his narrow escapes while hunting sperm whales. In one incident Bullen missed death by a whisker. He tells about it:

"Towering above me came the colossal head of the great creature, as he ploughed the bundle of debris that had just been a boat. There was an appalling roar of water in my ears, and darkness that might be felt all around. Yet, in the midst of it all, one thought predominated as clearly as if I had been turning it over in my mind in the quiet of my bunk aboard—'What if he should swallow me?' Nor to this day can I understand how I escaped the portals of his gullet, which of course gaped as wide as a church door. But the agony of holding my breath so overpowered every other feeling and thought, till just as something was going to snap inside my head I rose to the surface. I was surrounded by a welter of bloody froth, which made it impossible for me to see; but oh, the air was sweet!

"I struck out blindly, instinctively, although I could feel so strong an eddy that voluntary progress was out of the question. My hand touched and clung to a rope, which immediately towed me in some direction—I neither knew nor cared whither. Soon the motion ceased, and, with a seaman's instinct, I began to haul myself along by the rope I grasped, although no definite idea was in my mind as to where it was attached. Presently I came butt up against something solid, the feel of which gathered all my scattered wits into a compact knub of dread. It was the whale! 'Any port in a storm,' I murmured, beginning to haul away again on my friendly line. By dint of hard work I pulled myself right up the sloping, slippery bank of blubber, until I reached the iron, which, as luck would have it, was planted in that side of the carcass

This picture, "Firing a bomb lance," showing earliest form of harpoon gun, is from Bullen's *The Cruise of the Cachalot*

now uppermost. Carcass, I said—well, certainly I had no idea of there being any life remaining in the vast mass beneath me; yet I had hardly time to take a couple turns round myself with the rope (or whale-line, as it had proved to be), when I felt the great animal quiver all over, and begin to forge ahead. I was now composed enough to remember that help could not be far away, and that my rescue, providing that I should keep above water, was but a question of a few minutes. But I was hardly prepared for the whale's next move. Being very near his end, the boat, or boats, had drawn off a bit, I supposed, for I could see nothing of them. Then I remembered the flurry.

Almost at the same moment it began; and there was I, who with fearful admiration had so often watched the titanic convulsions of a dying cachalot, actually involved in them. The turns of harpoon line were off my body, but I was able to twist a couple of turns round my arms, which, in case of his sounding I could readily let go.

"Then all was lost in roar and rush, as of the heart of some mighty cataract, during which I was sometimes above, sometimes beneath, the water, but always clinging, with every ounce of energy still left, to the line. Now, one thought was uppermost—'What if he should breach?' I had seen them do so when in a flurry, leaping full twenty feet in the air. Then I prayed.

"Quickly as all the preceding changes had passed came perfect peace. There I lay, still alive, but so weak that, although I could feel the turns slipping off my arms, and knew that I should slide off the slope of the whale's side into the sea if they did, I could make no effort to secure myself. Everything then passed away from me, just as if I had gone to sleep.

"I do not at all understand how I kept my position, nor how long, but I awoke to the blessed sound of voices, and saw the second mate's boat alongside. Very gently and tenderly they lifted me into the boat, although I could hardly help screaming with agony when they touched me, so bruised and broken up did I feel. My arms must have been nearly torn from their sockets, for the strands of the whale-line had cut deep into their flesh with the strain upon it, while my thigh was swollen enormously from the blow I received at the onset."

Mariner-writer Bullen was indeed fortunate, because he lived to write about his adventures on the whaler *Cachalot*.

"John Tabor's Ride" from *History of the Whale Fishery* by J. Ross Browne, 1846

An occupation as colorful, violent, and hazardous as old-time whaling was bound to give rise to countless tales of encounters between men and their adversaries. Some of them, it is suspected, are only yarns spun by lamp light in the fo'c's'l, then bequeathed from one generation to another, with each narrator adding a detail or two of his own. In some cases of whaling tales handed down by word of mouth, it no longer is possible to separate fact from fancy.

Among the stories which we can be sure are in the realm of fancy is that of John Tabor. According to his yarn, he was one of the luckiest whaling men who ever lived. Supposedly lost far out in the Pacific while his ship was sperming, Tabor met a friendly cachalot, climbed upon the animal's back, and was given a swift ride home, all the way around Cape Horn.

All these stories, fact or fancy, comprise the fascination of the sea. Woven into this allurement, like angry red threads through a tapestry, are the cachalots, sometimes victors and more often the vanquished, smashing whaleboats and spouting their blood, but always majestic, warrior whales, even in death.

5. Early History of Sperming

If we look back to very old writings, we learn that the Phoenicians, an ancient people who had migrated to the shores of the Mediterranean Sea, developed a whaling industry more than a thousand years before the birth of Christ. Those Phoenician whalers may have been the first men to throw a harpoon at a cachalot.

When King Tiglath-Pileser I of Assyria swept down from the north to the Phoenician colonies on the shores of the Mediterranean in 1100 B.C., he discovered what was to him a strange industry among the inhabitants. The Phoenicians were putting to sea in oar-propelled vessels to hunt great animals which swam in the Mediterranean. The victim was referred to as a *nakhiru*, an Assyrian word meaning the "blower" and believed to indicate a sperm whale.

Ancient writings known as cuneiform inscriptions, carved in stone, tell how King Tiglath-Pileser was so fascinated that he set sail from the port of Arvad aboard a Phoenician vessel and witnessed the killing of a whale. The king was so impressed by the Phoenicians' whaling accomplishments that he carried enthusiastic word of it home, where it became a topic of lively discussion among the Assyrians for the next two centuries.

The Assyrians were an aggressive people, conquering those nations which resisted their armies. It must have been a surprise to them that the seafaring Phoenicians did not resist but laid down their arms and quietly joined them. They became part of the

The art of carving on whale's teeth, which began with the Phoenicians, centuries later became known as scrimshaw. These pictures show various jobs aboard a nineteenth-century whaler

Assyrian Empire, and, as was the custom in those days, paid tribute to the conquering kingdom. For the Phoenicians, part of the tribute consisted of teeth from *nakhiru* or sperm whales.

The teeth paid in tribute by the Phoenicians were not in the crude state, just as they had been pried from the cachalot's jaws. In addition to their ability as mariners, the Phoenicians were highly skilled craftsmen, specializing in meticulously beautiful work with ivory. Elephant ivory was extremely rare at that time and the "ivory" used by the Phoenicians was that of sperm whale's teeth. Among the wealthy and nobility at home and abroad there was much demand for the products of that superb workmanship. Centuries later this carving and embellishing of whale's teeth came to be known as scrimshaw.

As far back as the days of the Phoenicians, oil was a commodity sought in whaling, along with the teeth which figured so prominently in that ancient peoples' artistry. Sperm whaling, however, seems to have undergone a decline after the Phoenicians.

Ancient Chinese and Arabian books mention the cachalot, not as something to be hunted but as a formidable sea monster. In Greece the great philosopher Aristotle, who lived from 384 to 322 B.C. and has been called the father of biology and medicine, knew about the sperm whale. He called the giant beast *Phalaena*. Pliny the Elder, a Roman naturalist who perished in the fiery destruction of Pompeii by Mount Vesuvius in A.D. 79, also knew about the cachalot. He stated that the Physeter (sperm whale) "is the most bulky inhabitant, raising itself aloft like some vast column, as it towers above the sails of ships, belching forth as it were a deluge of water."

Whaling in general, but not sperm whaling, continued. Various peoples such as Norsemen, Basques, Japanese, English, and Dutch sailed away to hunt the sea giants. Among these monsters a species known as the right whale came to be the right target. Eventually the right whales were all but wiped out by the growing number of whaling ships.

In North America, whaling had its birth among the Indians. When Dutch and English settlers arrived in the New World in the sixteen hundreds, they found the Indians of Long Island, in the colony that was to be called New York, practicing a crude

Mox harpæ cetus funesta vulnera sentit.
Viribus utq potest arripit ille fugam.
Nunc vise extollit, nunc in profunda resultat.
Attamen insequitur hostis avarus eum.

Cursus balænarum harpá jam infixavel
insidere carro manuductili Hispanico.
Das Lauffe des Wallfischerdader Harpoen
soll stecktvoordas Sche ain Vo Span Schiffchen.

So bald er grosse Wall vermwundes sich empfindet.
Ein schneller Lauff die Flucht zu suchen voranient
Bald surchtet er in die Höh, bald in die Tieffe grimdet.
Doch ingescheinet ihn verfolgen seine Freind.

Early picture of whaling operations. The legend, in both Latin and old German, says that no matter how the whale leaps and sounds, his enemies in the Spanish boats with the harpoon firmly fixed will capture him

kind of whaling. Termed shore whaling, it consisted of two phases. In one, the redmen simply waited for the sea to cast a dead whale upon the beaches. In a more active phase, squaws and old men were posted atop high dunes to watch for any beasts coming close inshore. When one appeared and a signal was given, crews of sturdy warriors hurriedly put out to sea in dugouts or canoes. Pursuing the whale, the attackers endeavored either to kill their victim with spears or drive him into shallow water where the now-helpless animal could be dispatched more easily.

Some of the redmen were content with only the tails and flippers of the whales they slew, which they offered to their gods as tokens of respect. Other Indians sought food and medicinal help. It is recorded that the aborigines believed the cachalot's spermaceti to be particularly good medicine.

Soon the redmen and colonists had joined forces in shore whaling. The Indians had the right idea, the settlers recognized, but their gear and methods were primitive. The colonists set out to improve both. One of the first things they did was replace the Indians' crude spears with metal-tipped harpoons. Another refinement was the creation of a rugged, seaworthy craft designed specifically for whaling. The result was a whaleboat, so well planned that her design was not changed appreciably in the two hundred years that followed.

The shore whaling picture was to change radically. Fewer and fewer of the big animals came close enough to the beach to be pursued by whaleboats launched from shore. The hunters had to build larger vessels as they were forced farther and farther seaward to find their prey.

In 1712 occurred an incident which ushered in what was to become the most exciting, colorful, and often most violent chapter of an old industry.

In that year Captain Christopher Hussey of Nantucket commanded a small boat, on the open sea, in which he and eleven men pitted their cunning against the power and ferocity of a very large bull cachalot. The battle was relatively brief, as such encounters go, but for every second the lives of twelve humans were at stake. Unhesitatingly the intrepid whalers plunged their lances into the animal's huge body. It was perhaps this courage which saved their lives, for the mighty monster died before he could charge the boat or renew his air supply for a deep dive. Then came an equally

Early Dutch whaling scene, c. 1645

remarkable sequel to the contest. The rugged men towed the enormous carcass of the dead bull through rip tides and currents all the way to the harbor at Nantucket.

A record of the incident says quite simply:

"When lost in an open boat one Captain Christopher Hussey of Nantucket struck and killed a sperm whale which when tryed-out proved to be extremely valuable." By "tryed-out" (tried-out), the record meant that the cachalot's blubber had been cooked to extract its oil. The oil of that bull cachalot killed by Captain Hussey was a fortunate bounty for Nantucket. What no one could realize then was that Captain Hussey's conquest launched America on a course which was to take her to the pinnacle of whaling throughout the world.

Picture of "Trying Out" from *Nimrod of the Sea*, 1874

That was the "first shot," so to speak, in an industry which had been mainly dormant for about three thousand years. So far as is known, no whaler since the Phoenicians, in the time of King Tiglath-Pileser of Assyria, had attempted to capture the belligerent, deep-diving cachalot on the open sea and turn the event into an industry.

After Captain Hussey's successful kill, Yankee whalers quickly turned to sperming. Soon American whalers sailed from ports such as New Bedford, Sag Harbor, and Nantucket to high adventure, wealth, and fame on the furthest oceans of the world.

In that day the Lord with his hard, and great, and strong sword shall visit leviathan the bar serpent, and leviathan the crooked serpent, and shall slay the whale that is in the sea . . . Isaias

6. Sperm Whale and Man

Captain Christopher Hussey's bold harpooning of a big bull cachalot in 1712 literally launched a thousand ships—whaling ships and their whaleboats. Soon the battle cry of "A dead whale or a stove boat!" was heard ringing out over the restless seas, meaning that the whalers would capture a whale or get their boat crushed in the attempt. The cachalot was now the primary adversary.

Gradually, as the whalers' hunts carried them farther and farther from home ports, the sizes of their vessels increased to thirty, then fifty tons. In 1730, the first whaling schooner of seventy tons was launched. With these larger craft the sperming voyages grew longer and longer, venturing to the West Indies and the Caribbean, then to the Azores and beyond, even to the western seaboard of Africa, then back to South American waters.

The whaling industry was growing. But the vessels still were relatively small and rather crude. Rigged as schooners, they usually carried three masts. Their decks were cluttered with whaleboats, tools, gear, and the brick try works which contained two or more huge iron kettles in which whale blubber was boiled down into oil. The fire in these brick try works was started with wood, then kept going with the "crackling," an oily residue of the blubber which spilled from the iron kettles.

View of New Bedford on a whale's tooth

Officer's quarters were in the after section or stern of the vessel. The crew's quarters were in the forecastle, or "fo'c's'l" as it was called, in the forward section of the craft. These were cramped, dark, and almost airless, with three tiers of narrow board bunks for sleeping. Here the crewmen spent many of their off-hours, talking and swapping yarns about their adventures.

The remainder of the vessel below decks consisted of holds, or storage space. In these were kept ship's stores and provisions, along with casks to carry the whale oil. Her staterooms also contained harpoons, spare rigging, piles of sails, bricks for rebuilding the try works, iron hoops for clamping barrels together, and an assortment of miscellaneous items needed aboard a sailing ship.

Life on those early whaling vessels was exceedingly rough. The work was hard, broken only by periods of monotony. Thrown together in close quarters for months at

A New Bedford whaleboat hanging on davits on board schooner *John R. Manta*

Try pots used to "try out" blubber

a time, crewmen's tempers often flared. Under such conditions, often with food and water running low and disease creeping through the vessel, it is little wonder that many a seaman deserted his ship at the first opportunity.

Only a year or two before the great War for Independence from England, the American colonies' whaling fleet numbered between three hundred and four hundred ships, most of them operating out of New England ports. Far and wide these ships ranged in the search for cachalots.

During the Revolution, American whaling suffered severe setbacks. Many vessels were captured or sunk by the British. Communities which were dependent upon the whaling industry faced poverty. Even when the War for Independence was over and the colonies had won, the industry did little better, for then the British imposed a heavy tax on whale oil imported from America.

Despite such handicaps, however, the American whaling industry survived. By 1788, the fleet, again led by New Englanders, had begun its recovery. As the ships' numbers increased, so did their sizes. Now they could be fitted out for whale-hunting expeditions of two and three years. In 1791, American whalers braved the tempestuous waters off Cape Horn at the southernmost tip of South America and entered the Pacific Ocean. There they were surprised to discover that the Spaniards of Chile were carrying on a thriving whaling industry. They also learned that sperm whales were numerous off the western coast of South America and often came rather close inshore.

American whaling was yet to suffer another series of setbacks. One problem, at least for the infant republic's whaling port, was the harbor at Nantucket. There the difficulty lay in unloading cargoes brought back by whaling ships, because outside the harbor lurked treacherous sand bars and reefs, and entrance could be made only through a single narrow channel. Many of the larger vessels could not get through at certain times, and it finally became necessary to do the unloading and refitting of ships at nearby Martha's Vineyard.

The most serious setback of all was the War of 1812 with England. Again American whaling vessels fell prey to British warships and privateers. Others were commandeered by the American government to transport military personnel and equipment. Soon the greater part of the once-great whaling fleet had vanished; and by 1818 there were fewer than forty whalers left.

However, the end was not yet to ring down on American whaling. Yankee ships, in fact, concentrated even more on sperming. As the Massachusetts port of New Bedford took the lead, both in number of vessels and volume of whale products, ships were

Representation of whalers caught in the pack ice of the Arctic and abandoned, 1871

able to remain at sea for years, circling the world, if necessary, to find oil-rich cacha-lots. Meanwhile, the English, Scots, Dutch, Danes and others had entered the field, and competition in the hunt for sperm whales was increasing. The other countries extended their operations far afield, too. Some of the British whalers, for example, were venturing into the bleak stillness of the Arctic, braving terrible weather and the possibility of being crushed or imprisoned by vast ice packs. Then, in 1818, the first Americans sailed out into the remote Pacific coast regions to open new whaling grounds

Oil painting shows coopering of casks to hold whale oil aboard the bark *Greyhound*

around islands in the Galapagos, Christmas, Phoenix, and Gilbert groups.

The period from 1835 to 1860 often has been called the Golden Age of Whaling, for it was then that the industry as a whole reached its zenith. Sperming too was at its height, there being an ever-increasing demand for cachalot oil for lamps and candles.

In 1847 the American whaling fleet numbered some 594 vessels, valued in excess of

Men whose jobs were vitally important in whaling

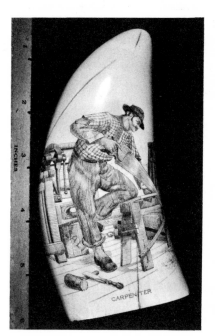

22 million dollars. About that time more than seventy thousand men were employed by the fleet, not counting those in such attendant shoreside occupations as cooperage or barrelmaking, shipyard work, sailmaking, provisioning, and so forth. During whaling's quarter-century golden era, the fleet caught about ten thousand sperm whales a year.

Among the larger whaling vessels was the strikingly handsome *Charles Morgan,* rated in the 500-ton category and measuring about 130 feet long from stempiece to transom. This proud ship is preserved in the Mystic Seaport, Mystic, Connecticut, along with other relics from a bygone era. A square-rigger carrying three masts, she was a rugged ship with a reinforced bow and sheathed sides. She was manned by a crew of thirty-two.

New Bedford was home to the *Charles Morgan*, and in the spring of 1849 she fitted out for a long sperming voyage. Aboard her went a seemingly endless procession of gear and provisions, including enough food for two years at sea. Also taken aboard were materials for repairing or replacing any equipment which might become broken or lost, as well as a supply of wood to fire the try works.

In her 32-man crew was a young New Bedford lad named Nelson Haley. Just seventeen, Haley was a harpooner, and there was nothing remarkable about him, not even his youth, for in those days many a lad went to sea at a more tender age. However, Nelson Haley is important to us because, thanks to his diary, he provides us with a glimpse of the emotions of a young sailor who is about to leave his home for a long time, possibly forever.

When the *Charles Morgan* departed New Bedford on June 8, 1849, to hunt cachalots in the far seas of the globe, young Nelson Haley wrote this entry in his private journal:

"I wonder when I shall see that lighthouse again, and New Bedford too. It may be the last time I shall see land while I am still so young. I am leaving a happy home behind me, my mother and my friends. I can see nothing ahead of me but hard work, storms, furious whales, and all sorts of dangers. I can't even give any reason why I

The *Charles W. Morgan* is now at Mystic, Connecticut

am leaving. It's not a question of money, certainly. Sailors never get rich. Mine is a strange kind of destiny."

Nelson Haley was not alone in such a mixture of emotions. Many mariners, even seasoned hands, experienced them as they saw home ports disappear astern over the horizon. But in his diary entry Nelson Haley was right on two counts: it was the last time he saw home while he was still so young; and ahead of him were storms, hard work, maddened whales, and all sorts of perils. The *Charles Morgan* did not return to New Bedford until May 25, 1853, four years later.

Aboard every whaling ship on a hunt there was a lookout aloft in a crow's-nest. From this vantage point he could scan the ocean for miles around, and his job was to watch for a great, dark back breaking the sea's surface, followed by the spouting which betrayed its owners' presence. Then came the cry from the rigging, "Thar she blows!" If the whale was a cachalot, the lookout added, "And sperm at that!"

This shout was the signal for the boat crews to swing into immediate action; and if a gam of whales had been sighted, the activity was fast and furious. Three to eight whaleboats might be lowered from the mother ship. Each comprised a pursuit and killer unit. Oarsmen, sometimes aided by a small sail, propelled the craft. A steerer handled the tiller which swung the rudder to guide the little vessel. In the bow, his long weapon ready, stood the harpooner. From his harpoon, and neatly coiled in a tub so that it could run free, ran the strong line which connected the weapon with the whaleboat. Once the harpooner had struck his victim, he changed places with the boat steerer and took over the tiller. The steerer, who usually was a mate on the ship, then went to the bow. His task was to kill the whale with a lance, a weapon some five feet long with an iron point shaped like a laurel leaf and razor-sharp on its edges.

In those days the harpoon did not kill the whale. Actually, its job was to secure the beast to the boat, much as a fishhook and line secure a fish for an angler. To make sure that it did not tear out when the whale surged forward, the harpoon's sharp head was equipped with barbs, much like those on fishhooks. When the animal felt the

The harpoon's sharp head was equipped with barbs to secure it in the whale

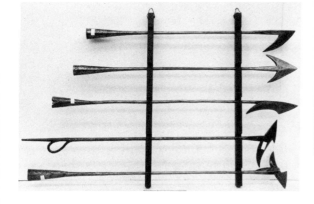

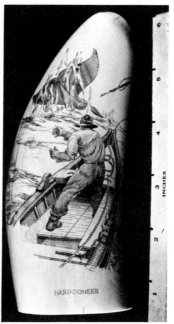

The harpooner and boatsteerer at work

pain of an iron harpoon sinking into his flesh, he suddenly developed a strong urge to go somewhere else. A harpooned cachalot instinctively wants to dive deep. But the desire to escape, the torment of pain, and the restriction of his movements all combine to keep him going in a forward, horizontal direction.

71

Then after him, out of its coil tub in the whaleboat, would race the harpoon line at express-train speed. The crew would try to slow the line as much as possible by taking a couple of turns with it around a loggerhead or wooden post in the boat. Often the speed and friction of the rope was such that it caused the wood to smoke, and it became necessary to douse it with water to prevent it from catching fire.

Mercy to the man who touched that rope with his bare hands, or let it rub against him anywhere. Instantly it could remove flesh or cut through clothing to inflict a serious burn. There was danger too in being caught by one of the loops of line as they whipped out of the tub. They could catch a man by the leg in a twinkling and pull him overboard to drown.

For the boat crews, the result of harpooning a cachalot was often a wild, fast ride which came to be known as a "Nantucket sleigh ride." After the whale was harpooned and secured, the real killing was done by driving the lance deep into a vital part of the animal. When the big beast "blew his blood," meaning he showed blood in his spoutings, the battle usually was over.

But the hard work continued when a carcass came alongside the mother ship for "flensing" or cutting the blubber. Swarming over the floating corpse, the men went to work to cut free the thick, oil-rich blubber in long strips about two feet wide. Block and tackle gear hoisted the heavy strips aboard the ship, where they were cut into pieces and fed into the try kettles for rendering.

During this process the head of the sperm whale was cut off and secured to the ship so that it rested nose down in the water. One of the crewmen would cut a piece about three feet in diameter from the head, a chunk known as the "case." The hole left

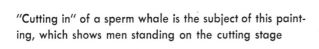

A "Nantucket sleigh ride," illustration from *The Cruise of the Cachalot*

"Cutting in" of a sperm whale is the subject of this painting, which shows men standing on the cutting stage

by the case was an entrance to the complete oil tank. A seaman was lowered into the liquid itself, which had enough body warmth to remain fluid. The tank is divided vertically by a thick membrane, and the crewman had to dive down into the oil, knife in hand, and cut his way through the membrane. He held a chain in his other hand,

Cutting in of a sperm whale on board bark
California

which he dragged through the hole and then looped onto itself. The sperm oil was then dipped out and stored.

Finally, in a welter of blood, the remains of the whale were cut free to become the food of sharks and other predators. This idea of processing the carcasses at sea aboard a "factory ship" has been credited to Francois Sapite, a Basque whaler.

The old-time hunters agreed that the cachalot was the most dangerous of all whales, the toughest to kill, and the one which took the longest to die. The animal's habit of "standing on his head" with his tail in the air before sounding, along with considerable agility despite his bulk, made him very dangerous to small, open boats. The greatest peril came from some of the older bulls, which put up a fierce resistance when harpooned and were even known to jump clear of the water, hitting the sea a thunderous slap with their tails. The enormous power and huge flukes of those tails could smash a whaleboat and her men with the ease of a fly swatter crushing a mosquito. There also was the danger of being rammed by an infuriated bull.

After 1846, American whaling skidded downhill. Some speed was lent to the decline by discovery of gold at Sutter's Mill, California, in 1849. Suddenly everyone developed "gold fever." Lured by the promise of fabulous wealth, thousands of men began a trek westward. With them went former whale hunters. There were no transcontinental railroads yet, and no Panama Canal. People traveled to the Pacific Coast by ship, braving storms and often hardships in months-long voyages around Cape Horn and up the western coast of South America. Transporting gold seekers became a profitable business, and a number of whalers converted to passenger vessels to cash in on the bonanza.

The Civil War, erupting in 1861, was an especially severe blow to American whaling. Men were siphoned from the industry for duty with the Union forces. Ships were converted to transports for military use; others fell victim to Southern warships and privateers. Certain foreign countries sympathizing with the South in the conflict seized still more whalers on one pretext or another. The whaling fleet diminished.

What was ultimately to be the death blow to American whaling was the discovery of petroleum at Oil Creek, Pennsylvania, in 1859. From petroleum was to come kerosene for lamps and stoves, and oils for lubricants, more easily available at a price

Left: Head of a sperm whale being taken on board the bark *California. Above:* Until the current goes off in modern times, people do not realize the inadequacy of lighting substitutes for electricity. These whale oil lamps were the best means of illumination prior to the discovery of petroleum

cheaper than sperm oil. (Many years later, when Thomas Alva Edison turned on an electric light switch in New York in 1882, he literally blew out the candles and oil lamps forever.)

As the 1800's closed, the American whaling fleet was dwindling rapidly. During the opening decade of the 1900's there were only four United States ports from which whalers sailed: New Bedford; San Francisco; Provincetown, Massachusetts; and Norwich, Connecticut. New Bedford still maintained its lead with twenty-four ships. Norwich had but one. A colorful chapter in American history was coming to an end; and in 1925, when the ships *Margarett* and *John R. Manta* returned to New Bedford, the curtain was lowered on the romantic era of sperm whaling in the United States.

But there are mementos of that heroic past. A living reminder of the early Indian and American sperming persists in the mid-Atlantic islands of the Azores. Among these isles are steep coasts surrounded by deep water, and sperm whales can approach quite close to shore. Even today those animals are pursued in oar-propelled boats and killed by hand-thrown harpoons; and some of the blubber is boiled in try kettles to extract its oil, just as in days past. At last count there were about fifteen land stations in operation, and the only innovation since bygone days of sperming is a motor launch to tow the boats out to the grounds and the whale carcasses back for flensing. Also, there is radio communication between the launch and lookout posts on land. Basically, this is shore whaling, just as American Indians practiced it on Long Island, New York, three centuries ago.

Other, more passive reminders of the past are in museums and private collections —the items of scrimshaw with which men whiled away the long hours at sea. They used baleen or whalebone, walrus tusks and cachalot teeth; and on them carved or etched delicate and often beautiful designs. To enhance their appearance further, lampblack, India ink, and sometimes colored pigments were worked into the designs. Sperm whale teeth usually were the favorite raw materials for scrimshaw, since they seemed best to represent savage and heroic adventure. The late President John F. Kennedy was an ardent collector of scrimshaw.

A sperm whale's tooth itself is highly valued even in these modern times. In 1953 when Queen Elizabeth II of the United Kingdom visited the Fiji Islands she was presented with one. In the Fijis, a cachalot's tooth is considered a great token of respect to offer visiting dignitaries.

Thus has the dark and enormous bulk of the sperm whale swum in and out of the

Two views of modern shore whaling in the Azores. Below, two whales are plainly visible. The light-colored sperm whale on the right is on its back, lower jaw sticking out of the water

life of man for countless hundreds of years, graciously but often violently, giving him light, heating his home, firing his stove, fueling his lighthouse beacons, furnishing entertainment in books and countless tales. Even today, the cachalots are playing a new but vital role in man's development of the last frontier on our globe, the sea.

In the year 1690 some persons were on a high hill
observing the whales spouting and sporting with each
other, when one observed; there—pointing to the
sea—is green pasture where our children's
grandchildren will go for bread . . . Obed Macy's History of Nantucket

7. Present Day Sperming

The quotation above dates back nearly three centuries; and now, more than ever, time is accenting the accuracy of Obed Macy's prophecy. In our fast-moving electronic age we may think of whales as belonging to the past. However, this is not so because the huge mammals still are of value to mankind, perhaps even more so than they were a century ago.

Only times have changed, not whales. They are still a prodigious source of high quality oil. Every day the modern world requires more oil to lubricate its machinery. Almost all airplanes use whale oil in their engines because it does not break down easily, flows freely at sub-zero temperatures, and is not destroyed by intense heat. Thus animals which have inhabited our seas for millions of years have "taken to the air" to become an important part of the jet age. Whale oil also is used in watches and precision machinery because it will lubricate even the smallest part, and one application may last a lifetime.

Nor are lubricants the only products of today's whaling operations. From whale oil modern chemistry extracts glycerin and basic ingredients important to the manufac-

Removing the "blanket piece" of a sperm whale, South Africa. Though many people think of whaling as a thing of the past, these mammals are still a prodigious source of oil

ture of cold cream, lipstick, and other cosmetics, as well as paint, varnishes, and textiles. A film of whale oil has been tried on the surfaces of reservoirs to cut down the water's evaporation to the atmosphere. From whale oil, margarine, an important food product, is made. Great Britain's entire margarine supply comes from whale oil.

Whalebone, when powdered, finds its way into fertilizers for farmers. The animal's internal organs, when processed, are used in food for cattle. Whale products are a part of modern medicine and nutrition, also. Oil from whale livers is far richer in vitamins

Cachalots still retain their status as prime targets because of the amount and quality of the oil they yield. Here flensing of a sperm whale has started as thick strip of blubber is peeled off. Note bloody trail to blubber hole

than cod liver oil. The pancreas, thyroid, and pituitary glands and liver are processed in pharmaceutical laboratories to yield hormones, enzymes, vitamins, insulin, the substance known as ACTH, and a number of other medicinal compounds.

A century has brought many, many changes to whaling; yet, as the killer fleets prowl the oceans in their search for blue whales, humpbacks, Sei whales, and others, cachalots retain their status as prime targets. Oil from sperm whale blubber still has the finest quality of all whale oil; and the average cachalot still yields more oil than any other species of equal bulk. And there is that big bonus in the form of the tankful of spermaceti encased in the outsized skull.

Cachalot oil is especially good in the manufacture of cosmetics; and spermaceti is used in the production of a number of ointments because it is absorbed readily by human skin. Unlike that of some species, the meat from sperm whales is considered inedible. However, the animals more than compensate for that shortcoming by yielding material for shoes, slippers, pocketbooks, film, bicycle seats, "gut" string for tennis racquets, and a host of other products. Cachalot teeth still are used, also. From them are made chessmen, buttons, and other "ivory" items.

There is an endless assortment of sperm whale memorabilia put to modern-day use. Some of the objects are utilitarian as well as decorative, such as whale oil lamps wired for electricity and place mats with colorful action scenes of sperm whaling. Purely decorative objects run from cachalots cast in pewter for wall decorations through jewelry and toys to exotic sperm whale ornaments of solid crystal.

Any creature can be hunted to near-extinction. It almost happened to the bison which once roamed the western prairies of the United States in huge herds. It did

Shooting at the circle of sperm whales shown on page 27

happen to the American passenger pigeon. Once those birds were so numerous that a single flock, according to an account, required four hours to fly over a given spot at a speed of sixty miles an hour. The slaughter of passenger pigeons was so heartless and thorough that finally only one was left, and that bird died in a Cincinnati, Ohio, zoo in 1914.

New Zealand Tory Channel launches in pursuit of whales

At one time certain species of whales were hunted perilously close to the brink of extinction, too, with the survivors retreating to far places where they could escape their relentless pursuers. In one region or another it happened to gray whales, cachalots, and right whales. As good fortune would have it, however, the whaling industry came to realize that unless the big beasts were protected by law, man would send them the way of the long-extinct dodo bird. Furthermore, such law and its enforcement could come about only through agreement among nations participating in whaling, since their vessels operate on open oceans which do not come under the jurisdiction of any one country.

Accordingly, in 1935, an International Whaling Commission was established. By agreement among the participating countries, the functions of this group would be to decide: How many whales could be killed annually without endangering any species; what months of the year hunting would be permitted; what ocean regions would be reserved as sanctuaries in which whaling would be prohibited; and which species could be captured and which should be protected. Equally important, the Commission set up a system of inspection and law enforcement to make sure protective restrictions were obeyed.

The Commission also has set minimum lengths for various species. Any smaller animals cannot be killed. The lower limit is thirty-five feet for sperm whales, except for South America, where the minimum is thirty feet. In practice, this means that nearly all cows are spared for breeding purposes to keep cachalot populations at a safe level.

It is to be wondered what old-time whaling skippers would think of today's operations. In essence the general procedure is the same. Smaller vessels are used for pursuit and do the actual killing, after which carcasses are brought to a mother ship for butchering. But there are other radical changes. Engine-powered vessels, sometimes called chasers, have replaced oar-powered whaleboats; and irons are fired from small cannons instead of flung by hand. An explosive charge, not a harpooner's lance, is the fatal instrument. Carcasses are dismantled aboard a big factory vessel instead of being flensed or cut up alongside the ship while still in the water.

The modern whaling unit is a small fleet of vessels. Hub of the unit, so to speak, is the mother or factory ship. The term "factory" is most appropriate, for she is a mass

The *hval kla* draws a baleen whale up the stern ramp of a factory ship

of machinery—power gear for stripping the carcasses, pressure cookers for processing blubber and meat, tanks for storing oil, even testing laboratories. Accompanying her are the chasers, which can number up to eight, ten, or more. Also in the fleet are buoy craft to mark the bodies of killed whales, as well as vessels to tow the carcasses to the factory ship. Each fleet also may include a tanker, which serves double duty by transporting oil and other products to the nearest port for shipping and then returning to the fleet with fuel and provisions.

Norway has been a leading developer of modern whaling procedures. Several of

Boat with whaling gun
ready to fire
  1—Norwegian whaling
      gun
  2—Gun trigger
  3—Harpoon
  4—Bomb

today's implements and techniques are the product of Norwegian inventiveness. One is an ingenious seizing device known as the whale claw, or *hval kla*. Activated by a powerful winch and a system of cables and pulleys, the claw grabs a whale carcass by its tail section for hauling aboard the factory ship. This device, along with the wide slipway or ramp in the stern of present factory ships, not only ended the dangerous practice of butchering the animals while they were still in the water but also made it possible to utilize as much of each carcass as is desirable, instead of removing only the blubber and baleen.

Flag marks position of a dead whale off coast of Alaska

The harpoon gun, conceived by Svend Foyn in 1868, has an accurate range up to about a hundred feet. Needless to say, there is immensely more force and consequently greater penetration in a gun-fired weapon than one hurled by an old-time harpooner. The explosive charge, or grenade, now incorporated in the war head has a time fuse which detonates it in the whale seconds after impact, thus making death quicker and more merciful.

There have been many changes made to expedite whaling. Just one on the long list involves a marking of carcasses so that they can be retrieved by other craft in the fleet, leaving the chasers to go about their business of pursuing other victims in a gam. In this simple method the unit's buoy boats implant a flag in each body, after which a towing vessel, sometimes called a corvette, collects the carcasses for towing to the factory ship. An even later refinement is a small radio transmitter which can be affixed

Large sperm whale on afterdeck of factory ship

to a dead whale. The little transmitter then sends out continuous radio signals which facilitate finding the carcass. This is especially helpful in fog or when the dead whale has drifted an appreciable distance. Still another refinement is the pumping of air into the bodies of species which might otherwise sink before they could be retrieved.

As the carcasses are collected by corvettes they are towed to the factory ship, and there left floating alongside her. As needed, each carcass then is maneuvered to the slipway or ramp at the vessel's stern. With the body now at the slipway, tail first, the mighty clutch of the whale claw takes over. Seizing the huge corpse by its tail section, the claw drags it up the sloping tunnel of the slipway and onto a large afterdeck. Here, in a kind of open-air "operating room," the late sea giant will be methodically dismantled.

First to attack the carcass is a group of flensers whose job it is to make major cuts in the blubber. Power equipment then peels it away in large strips. Now a second crew of flensers moves in. Theirs is the job of cutting the blubber into smaller sections. That accomplished, a third group takes over. These fellows are called blubber boys, and their task is simply to drag the strips of blubber along and feed them into special openings in the deck.

As they slither into the holes on deck, the blubber strips first pass through grinding machines which mash them into a kind of mushy pulp. From the grinders this pulp is fed into king-size pressure cookers, the modern descendants of the old on-deck try works. These pressure cookers, devised by a Finn named Nils Kvaener, operate on somewhat the same principle as their smaller counterparts in home kitchens. Using superheated steam under great pressure, they cook blubber until it disintegrates into a thick soup. Later that "soup" is centrifuged to extract just about every ounce of oil it contains. Pressure cookers also handle whale meat and bone, after which the cooked material can be centrifuged to remove its oil and then dried and put into bags for use in fertilizers and meals of various kinds.

Once the flensers have denuded a whale carcass of its blubber and removed its baleen, the remains are moved ahead to a forward deck, leaving the afterdeck clear for the next corpse.

On the forward deck the blubberless carcass is set upon by another crew of specialists called lemmers. These fellows are dissection experts, chosen for their ability to remove meat, bones, and certain organs with the greatest speed, minimum effort and least waste. Under their skillful ministrations the mountain of tissues rapidly dwindles to practically nothing as they cut away flesh and extract the liver and other

The flensers attack a sperm whale carcass. Note the blubber holes at left

desired glands. The meat vanishes into holes leading to other pressure cookers. The liver is cut up in a prescribed way; then that too disappears into the factory. Bones are cut into pieces by whining power saws and fed into still other openings leading to processing below decks. All things considered, relatively little of the carcass is discarded after the lemmers' operation. Even the blood and any scraps of flesh which may have accumulated are retrieved for processing. Finally, the minute remains of a once huge and majestic animal disappear as dirty water through the scuppers as the deck is hosed down.

Just as species, sizes, whaling grounds, and so forth are prescribed by law, so is the handling of whale carcasses dictated by specific rules. These are declared by a code titled *Whaling Industry, Ship Regulations, 1951*, which states: "All parts of whales delivered to the factory ship by ships attached thereto shall be processed by boiling or otherwise, except the internal organs, whalebone and flippers of all whales, the meat of sperm whales and of parts of whales intended for human food or feeding of animals."

Chile and Peru head the list for their sperming catches. Their ships account for 27 per cent of the total take. Antarctic waters surrender another 20 per cent; and 18 per cent of today's captured sperm whales are harpooned off Japan and Korea. Africa's southern offshore ocean regions are credited with 15 per cent; and the remaining 20 per cent of the catch is made in various other areas.

Men have hunted different kinds of whales for hundreds, perhaps thousands, of years; and since 1900 more than one million of the animals have been killed. The aggressive cachalots have been the true monarchs of them all, intriguing, awing, frightening, and even killing their pursuers, but always serving mankind.

Now we are in an exciting age of electronics and harnessed atomic energy. We take for granted such things as eventual spanning of the Atlantic Ocean by jet aircraft in two hours, and incredibly complex computers which can "think" and "remember." Even plans for colonizing the moon no longer cause raised eyebrows. Far in the background of these astounding accomplishments, and completely oblivious of them, swims the huge, dark-skinned beast we know as the sperm whale. His is an existence which began millions of years ago and has remained basically unchanged ever since. Yet between those two incongruous environments, the atomic-powered, jet-propelled era of humankind and the primaeval world of the cachalot, there still persists a link.

That tie has alternately strengthened, weakened, and strengthened again with the passage of centuries, but it has not broken. How long it will endure, no one can say,

Two pictures of harpooners at work
on modern ships

The harpoon flies toward an oil-rich target.

but it seems destined to last beyond the foreseeable future; and if we could stare into the next century it would not come exactly as a surprise to learn that in one way or another man's long-time cetacean benefactor still will be serving him. It might be only as a tiny drop of oil lubricating a delicate instrument, or perhaps as a capsule-size food-fortifier for outer space explorers, but it will be service nonetheless, just as vital as that of providing the illumination of a hundred years ago.

The warrior whale, long a part of man's exploitation of our planet's last frontier, the sea, may aid man in exploring space and the outer universe.

INDEX

ABOUT THE AUTHORS

JOSEPH J. COOK received his B.A. degree at Drake University and his M.S. from the State University College, New Paltz, New York, following three years in the Army during the second World War. He also attended Columbia University and has been a reading analyst for a major publishing house. Mr. Cook is a principal in the Island Trees School District of Long Island.

WILLIAM L. WISNER was for fifteen years managing editor and chief of writers of the fishing, boating, and marine natural history magazine *Sportsmen's Life*. He also has been outdoor columnist of the New York *World-Telegram & Sun*, as well as *Newsday*, Long Island's leading newspaper. In addition, for fifteen years he has written fishermen's programs for radio stations WCBS and WOR in New York and others on Long Island and in Connecticut. His college is Columbia University, and he is a lifelong fisherman and student of the sea.

Both authors are natives of Long Island, confirmed students of wildlife, and strong advocates of conservation. They have collaborated in *Your First Book of Salt Water Fishing, Killer Whale!* and *The Phantom World of the Octopus and Squid*, as well as on *Warrior Whale*.